It's another Quality Book from CGP

This book has been carefully written for Year 5 children learning science. It's full of questions and investigations designed to cover the Year 5 objectives on 'Living things and their habitats' and 'Animals, including humans' from the latest National Curriculum.

There's also plenty of practice at 'Working Scientifically' throughout the book.

What CGP is all about

Our sole aim here at CGP is to produce the highest quality books — carefully written, immaculately presented and dangerously close to being funny.

Then we work our socks off to get them out to you — at the cheapest possible prices.

Contents

Answers to the questions are on the back of the Pull-out Poster in the centre of the book.

Published by CGP

Contributors
Charlotte Burrows, Sarah Pattison, Camilla Simson, Sean Stayte
With thanks to Katie Braid, Jill Cousner and Camilla Simson for the proofreading.

ISBN: 978 1 78294 088 3

Clipart from Corel®
Printed by Elanders Ltd, Newcastle upon Tyne.
Based on the classic CGP style created by Richard Parsons.

Text, design, layout and original illustrations © Coordination Group Publications Ltd. (CGP) 2014
All rights reserved.

Photocopying this book is not permitted, even if you have a CLA licence.
Extra copies are available from CGP with next day delivery • 0800 1712 712 • www.cgpbooks.co.uk

Sexual Reproduction in Animals

New baby animals are made by <u>sexual reproduction</u>.
It's where a <u>sperm</u> fertilises an <u>egg</u> and the fertilised egg <u>grows</u> into a baby animal.

1. Use **some** of the words in the box to fill in the gaps below.

fertilised	sexual	egg	animal	asexual	sperm

   New animals are made by .... reproduction.

   This is where an .... inside the mother is

   .... by a .... from the father.

2. (Circle) the adult animals that can make a kitten by **sexual reproduction**.

   A female cat   A male cat and a female cat   Three male cats

3. Which two things are **needed** to make a baby by sexual reproduction?
   (Circle) the correct pair.

   Two eggs   Two sperm   An egg and a sperm

4. Write **1-4** in the boxes to put the stages of sexual reproduction in order.
   I've done the first one for you.

   The embryo develops into a baby animal. ☐   The egg is fertilised by the sperm. ☐

   The egg and the sperm meet. [1]   The fertilised egg grows into an embryo. ☐

Sexual Reproduction in Animals

5.   Draw lines to show which pairs of animals can make babies by **sexual reproduction**.

A male lion

A male chicken

A female cow

A male rabbit

A male rabbit

A male tortoise

A female lion

A female chicken

Circle the animals above that produce **sperm**.

6.   Write **true** or **false** next to each of these sentences.

The sperm comes from the female animal. ....

The egg comes from the male animal. ....

The egg is fertilised by the sperm. ....

The fertilised egg grows into an embryo. ....

Now rewrite the sentences you marked as false, so that they're **correct**.

....

....

....

....

INVESTIGATE ....

- Choose an animal from question 5 and make a poster to show the stages of sexual
- reproduction for this animal. Write down each stage that happens and then finish it with
- a drawing of the baby animal. Look back at question 4 for help with the different stages.

                                              © CGP — not to be photocopie

Sexual Reproduction in Plants

Plants also use sexual reproduction to make <u>new plants.</u> In plants, an <u>egg</u> is fertilised by <u>pollen</u>, not sperm. The <u>seed</u> that is made then grows into a new plant.

1.   Use the words in the box to fill in the labels on the flower.

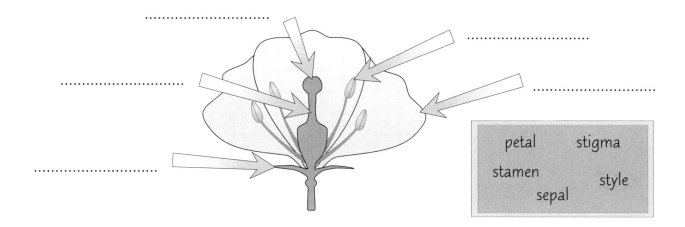

petal	stigma
stamen	
	style
sepal	

2.   Label this flower in the same way as the one above.
      Make sure you label the **petals**, **sepals**, **stamen**, **stigma** and **style**.

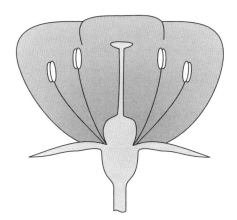

3.   (Circle) the right words to complete these sentences.

      Insect-pollinated flowers have large bright **petals / stamen** to attract insects.

      The stamen of wind-pollinated flowers hang **inside / outside** the flower

      to release pollen on the slightest breeze. The stigma is sticky in

      insect-pollinated flowers to collect the **pollen / style** from the bees.

Sexual Reproduction in Plants

4. One of these diagrams shows pollination, the other shows fertilisation.
    The thin arrows show the direction the pollen is going in each one.
    Label each diagram **pollination** or **fertilisation**.

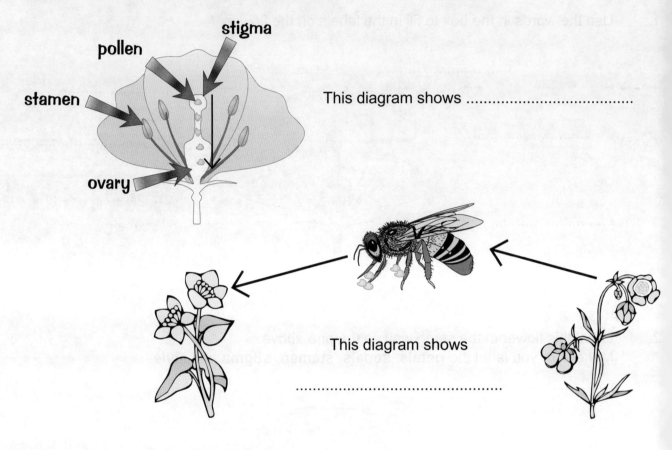

This diagram shows ....

This diagram shows

....

5. Fill in the gaps using the words from the box.

| sizes | tiny | wide area | fruit | pollen | seeds |

Plants disperse .... grains of .... to fertilise

other plants of the same type so they can make .... Seeds come

in all different shapes and ...., some are even surrounded in

heavy .... Plants also disperse their seeds to spread them over

a .... and make sure there are lots more plants like them.

© CGP — not to be photocopie

Sexual Reproduction in Plants

6. Write **1-4** in the boxes to put these pictures of **sexual reproduction** in order.
    I've done one for you.

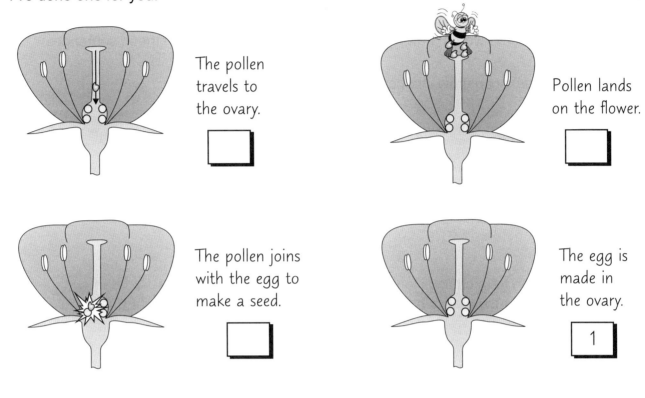

The pollen travels to the ovary.

[ ]

Pollen lands on the flower.

[ ]

The pollen joins with the egg to make a seed.

[ ]

The egg is made in the ovary.

[1]

Write down the number of the picture that shows **fertilisation**. ....

7. For each pair of words in brackets, (circle) the one that makes the sentence right.

Sexual reproduction is one way that a **(new / parent)** plant makes **(new / parent)** plants. It includes **(pollination / germination)** and **(circulation / fertilisation)**.

Pollination is when the pollen from the **(stamen / stigma)** of one flower is taken to the **(stamen / stigma)** of another flower.

Fertilisation is when the **(stamen / pollen)** travels down into the **(stamen / ovary)** and joins with an egg to form a seed.

The **(seed / pollen)** grows into a new plant.

INVESTIGATE ....

Using question 6, write down the stages of sexual reproduction of plants. Compare them to the stages of sexual reproduction in animals (look back at Q4 on page 1 for help) and make a list of the differences between them. Are there any similarities?

© CGP — not to be photocopied

Asexual Reproduction in Plants

Some plants can make new plants __without__ pollen or eggs — this is called __asexual reproduction__.
It's where a little bit of the __old plant__ grows into a __new plant__.

1. Use some of the words growing on the **plant** to fill in the gaps in these sentences.

    Some plants can grow into new plants without ....

    or an .... Instead, a whole new plant grows

    from a .... of the old plant. This is called

    .... reproduction.

    (word leaves on plant: sexual, egg, pollination, asexual, little bit)

2. Plants grown from cuttings look the **same** as the parent plant.
    Circle all the **new plants** below that were grown from the parent plant.

    Parent plant   A   B   C   D   E

3. Put a tick (✔) next to all the sentences that describe **asexual** reproduction.

    Growing new plants from   A bee taking pollen from
    cuttings of a parent plant. ☐   one flower to another. ☐

    Growing new plants   Growing new plants
    from seeds. ☐   from bulbs. ☐

<u>*INVESTIGATE*</u> . . . .

• *Create an information leaflet for gardeners explaining the differences between sexual*
• *and asexual reproduction in plants. For example, which type of reproduction uses eggs*
• *and pollen? Which type involves cuttings? Does asexual reproduction need fertilisation?*

. . . .

          © CGP — not to be photocopied

Taking Cuttings

 MINI-PROJECT

> Gardeners take cuttings from old plants and use them to grow new plants. In this project you'll do an experiment to find out which bits of a plant you can grow new plants from.

1. Write down the name of the **parent plant** that you will use in your experiment.

   (I've put some suggestions in the box on the right.)

   ....

Geranium	Mint
Busy Lizzie	Tomato

2. Write **root**, **stem** or **leaf** in the gaps below to complete the **method** for taking a cutting.

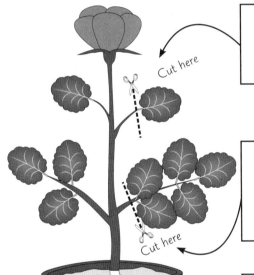

Cut here

Taking A .... Cutting
1. Choose a new, healthy leaf.
2. Cut straight across using sharp scissors.

Cut here

Taking A .... Cutting
1. Choose a stem with new growth.
2. Cut the stem just above a leaf.
3. Remove most of the leaves.

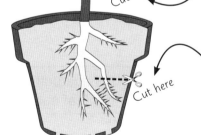

Cut here

Taking A .... Cutting
1. Scoop out some soil to expose the roots.
2. Cut off a length of new root growth.
3. Cover the roots back over with soil.

3. Which cuttings do you predict will **grow**? Tick (✔) the boxes below.

   Root cutting   Stem cutting   Leaf cutting

   Now take your cuttings. Try to keep the cuts as straight as possible.

   Be careful with those sharp scissors.

© CGP — not to be photocopied

MINI-PROJECT

Taking Cuttings

Now that you have your cuttings, you can **plant** them.
Read these **instructions** carefully and then follow them for each of your cuttings.

1. Fill a small plant pot with **moist** compost.
   Make sure it has **holes** in the bottom so water can drain out.

2. Use a pencil to make a **hole** in the compost
   that's big enough for the cutting.

   You'll have to plant the root cutting a bit differently — see the diagram below.

3. Put the cutting in the hole and gently **pat down** the compost.
   Your potted cuttings should look like this:

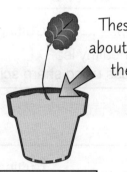

These ends are about <u>1 cm</u> below the surface.

Stem cutting

Leaf cutting

Plant the root cutting so that the <u>top</u> of the root is just <u>below</u> the surface of the compost.

Root cutting

4. Place the pot in a **clear** plastic bag and **seal it** with an elastic band.

5. Put the pot somewhere with plenty of **light**.

> Now **repeat** steps 1 – 5 until you have potted
> a **root** cutting, a **stem** cutting and a **leaf** cutting.

4. Here is a method for **looking after** your cuttings.
   Circle the words in brackets that are **correct**.

   Every two (**seconds** / **days**) for ten weeks, remove the

   plastic bag from each pot and shake off any water.

   Add more water to the compost if it is (**wet** / **dry**).

        © CGP — not to be photocopied

Taking Cuttings

5. Leave your cuttings to grow for **10 weeks**.
After 10 weeks, draw a picture of each of the cuttings.

Root cutting:

Stem cutting:

Leaf cutting:

6. Did all of your cuttings **grow**? (Circle) your answer.   **yes** / **no**

If not, which cuttings **didn't grow** at all?

....

7. Look at your answer to question 3. Was your prediction **right**? ....

8. If your cuttings grew, measure the **length** of each cutting using a ruler.
Which cutting grew the **most**? Complete the sentences below.

HINT: check out the whole length of your cuttings by gently digging them out of the compost.

The .... cutting grew the most.

It is .... cm long.

EXTRA PROJECT

Repeat the experiment with cuttings from a different plant.
Write a prediction of which cuttings will grow — do you think the results will be the same?

Section 2 — Life Cycles

Life Cycles of Mammals

All animals start off life as just tiny <u>fertilised eggs</u>. When a <u>mammal</u> egg is fertilised it grows <u>inside</u> the mother, so the mammal is born as a <u>live baby</u>.

1. Circle the animals below that are **mammals**.

2. The life cycle of a mammal starts with a fertilised egg.
   Complete this diagram of a cat's life cycle by writing **cat** and **kitten** in the right boxes.

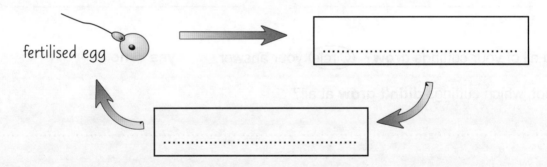

fertilised egg

....

....

3. Tick (✔) the sentence below that **does not** describe a stage in the mammal life cycle.

The mother gives birth to live babies.	The baby hatches from an egg.	The baby develops inside its mother.
☐	☐	☐

INVESTIGATE ·

Choose your favourite mammal. Make a poster to tell people about its life cycle. Include as much information about each stage as you can. Use the Internet or books to help you.

 © CGP — not to be photocopied

Life Cycles of Birds

The life cycle of a bird starts when the mother bird lays an <u>egg</u>.
The baby bird develops <u>inside</u> the egg until it is ready to hatch.

1. Write **1-5** in the boxes to put the **life cycle** of a **chicken** in order.
   I've done the first one for you.

   [ ]   [1]   [ ]   [ ]   [ ]

2. Here are some sentences about the **life cycle** of a **penguin**.

   (A) The chick hatches from the egg.   (B) The chick grows into an adult penguin.

   (C) The penguin lays a fertilised egg.   (D) The chick develops inside the egg.

   Put the sentences in order by writing the letters below.

   ....

3. Many birds hatch from eggs in nests that are **high up**
   off the ground to keep them safe from **predators**.
   The **Dodo** was a bird alive hundreds of years ago.
   It lived on a small island with few animals.

   A predator is an animal that <u>kills and eats</u> other animals.

   The Dodo laid its eggs in a nest on the **ground**. **Why** might it have done that?

   ....

INVESTIGATE •

*Draw a diagram to show what you think the life cycle of a blackbird might be like. Draw
a picture for each stage. To start with think about what a bird hatches from. Afterwards,
look up a blackbird's life cycle in a book or on the Internet. Is your life cycle right?*

© CGP — not to be photocopied   *Section 2 — Life Cycles*

Life Cycles of Insects

The life cycle of an insect starts with an <u>egg</u>. When it hatches, the young insect often doesn't look like the adult. Its body <u>changes</u> a lot as it <u>grows</u>.

1.   Butterflies are insects. Fill in the labels for **life cycle** of a **butterfly** using the words in the box.

| butterfly   caterpillar   eggs   chrysalis |

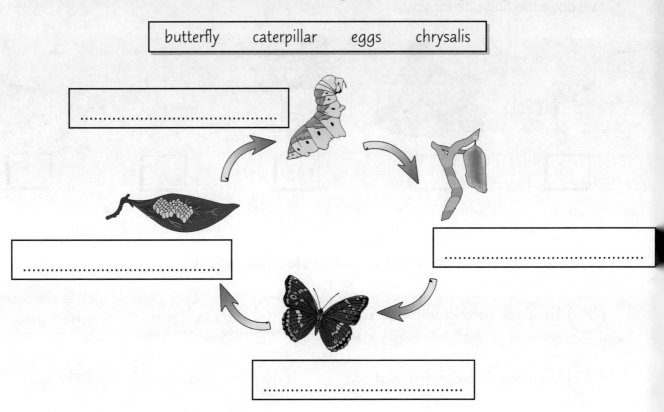

....

....

....

....

2.   The picture on the right shows the **life cycle** of a **beetle**.
Circle the correct words in **bold** to complete
these sentences about the beetle life cycle.

Eggs are laid by the [**larva** / **adult**].

An egg hatches into a [**larva** / **worm**].

The larva has [**lots of** / **no**] wings.

The pupa stage is between the larva and [**egg** / **adult**] stages.

adult beetle

eggs

pupa

larva

INVESTIGATE •

• *Make models of the stages of the butterfly life cycle using plasticine or clay, or by cutting*
• *out a picture from cardboard. Use your models to help you to explain the life cycle of a*
• *butterfly to a friend. When you're finished, ask your friend to put the stages in order.*
• •

                                          © CGP — not to be photocopied

Life Cycles of Amphibians

Adult amphibians live on <u>land</u> but most lay their eggs in <u>water</u>. When they hatch from the eggs, young amphibians have <u>gills</u> and live <u>underwater</u>. They develop their <u>lungs</u> as they grow into adults.

1. The life cycle of a **frog** is shown below.

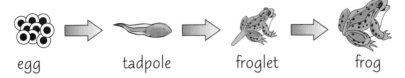

egg　　　　tadpole　　　froglet　　　frog

Use the words on the lilypad to complete these sentences about a frog's life cycle.

The adult frog lays its eggs in a .... The eggs

hatch into tadpoles, which have .... and tails

for .... As they grow, the tadpoles develop

.... and their tails begin to ....

— at this stage they are called ....

The froglets develop .... and leave the water as .... frogs.

lungs, gills, shrink, legs, adult, swimming, froglets, pond

2. Look at the line graph on the right. Why does the amount of frogs get **bigger** as the amount of tadpoles gets **smaller**?

    ....

    ....

    The pond has **no tadpoles** in January, but by April it has **lots**. Where did the tadpoles come from?

    ....

    ....

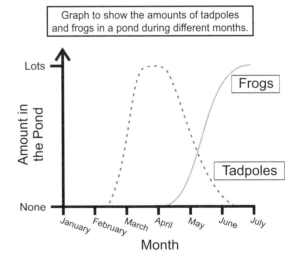

Graph to show the amounts of tadpoles and frogs in a pond during different months.

INVESTIGATE

Write a story about the life of a frog, from the point of a tadpole hatching from an egg to the adult frog laying its own eggs. Describe how its body changes as it grows, and explain the life stages it goes through to become an adult frog. You can use question 1 to help you.

Life Cycles of Animals

All animals are <u>born</u> and <u>reproduce</u>, but their <u>life cycles</u> can be very different.
For example, some are born as <u>live babies</u> and others hatch from <u>eggs</u>.

1. (Circle) the animals that **lay eggs**.

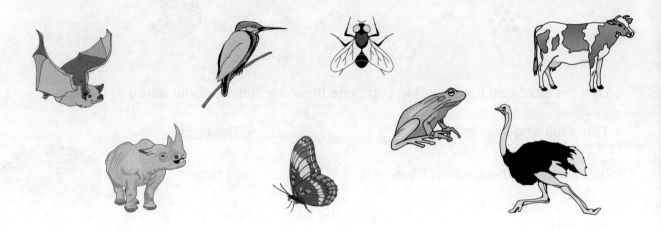

2. The table below contains information about the **life cycles** of four different animals.

Animal name	Does it hatch from an egg?	Name for its young	Average Lifespan	Age when it can reproduce	Number of eggs laid by the adult
Mosquito	Yes	Larva	30-40 days	7-8 days	45 - 200
Fruit bat	No	Pup	20-30 years	5-20 months	0
Kite	....	....	8-10 years	2-3 years	1 - 4

A kite is a type of **bird**. Use what you know about the bird life cycle to **fill in** the table.

Which of the animals in the table has the **shortest** lifespan? ....

Which of the animals in the table has the **longest** lifespan? ....

Which of the animals in the table is a **mammal**? ....
How can you tell? Write down **one** reason.

....

Answers to Y5 'Life Cycles and Reproduction'

2. childhood
    The gaps should show the names and stages of people known by the person doing the question.

3. goes to primary school — B
    has children that go to school — D
    learns to read and write — B
    doesn't go to work any more — E
    body starts changing at puberty — C
    can't walk yet — A

4.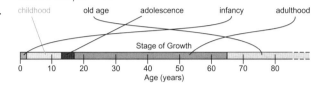
    The arrow should point to the position on the timeline that the person doing the question is at.

5. Janet — old age
    Jayden — childhood
    Rob — adulthood
    Tommy — infancy

Pages 20-21 — Puberty

1. Her breasts will develop. / She will start having periods.
2. 'The body stops growing' should be circled.
3. ovaries, month, begin
4. E.g. you should have drawn facial hair on Mark.
5. adolescence
6. sperm
    E.g. His voice will get deeper.
    Hair will start to grow on his body.
    Hair will start growing on his face.
7. true, false, true, false
    E.g. boys and girls grow body hair, girls and boys develop bigger muscles.

Page 22 — Humans and Other Animals

1. human
2. elephant
3. sheep, elephant, horse
4. sheep
5. human

Pages 23-25 — Measuring Human Growth

1. To check that they are growing at the right speed.
2. Clothes and nappies add extra mass.
3. 7 kg
4. higher
5. E.g. because wearing different types of shoes adds different amounts to people's heights.
6. Put names in a hat and pick them out at random.
7. The tables should be filled in using results collected by you, or using all/some of the spare results.

8. Depends on your results. This table uses the spare results.

Height (cm)	Number of Girls		Number of Boys	
	Tally	Total	Tally	Total
110 - 119		0	II	2
120 - 129	II	2	III	3
130 - 139	IIII	4	III	3
140 - 149	III	3	I	1
150 - 159	I	1	I	1

9. Depends on your results.
    These bar charts use the spare results.

    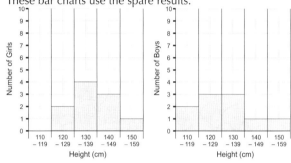

10. Depends on your results.
    For the spare results, girls were taller overall.

Mixed Questions — Pages 26-29

1.

2. All animals are born as live babies.
3. fertilised, grows, female, sperm, ovary, pollen, seed
4. gooseberry bush, sunflower, dandelion
5. infancy, childhood, adolescence, adulthood, old age
6.

    The pollen in made in the stamen.
7. fertilisation
8. From the top left: eggs, tadpole, froglet, frog.
9.

Girls	Boys	Both
Breasts develop.	Grow facial hair.	Growth spurts.
	Start making sperm.	Grow underarm hair.

10. 2. The seed is moved away from the parent plant.
    3. The seed grows into a seedling.
    4. The seedling grows into an adult plant.
11. C
    E.g. It only has three stages, it doesn't have a pupa stage.
12. When part of an old plant grows into a new plant.
    E.g. strawberries grow new plants from runners, daffodils grow new plants from bulbs.

REPRODUCTION

Animals reproduce by sexual reproduction.

Birds hatch from eggs.

Caterpillars turn into butterflies.

Life cycle of a frog.

Answers to Y5 'Life Cycles and Reproduction'

Section 1 — Reproduction

Pages 1-2 — Sexual Reproduction in Animals

1. sexual, egg, fertilised, sperm
2. 'A male cat and a female cat' should be circled.
3. 'An egg and a sperm' should be circled.
4. 2. The egg is fertilised by the sperm.
   3. The fertilised egg grows into an embryo.
   4. The embryo develops into a baby animal.
5. A male lion — A female lion
   A male chicken — A female chicken
   All the male animals should be circled.
6. false, false, true, true
   E.g. the sperm comes from the male animal.
   E.g. the egg comes from the female animal.

Pages 3-5 — Sexual Reproduction in Plants

1.
2.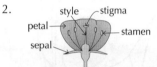
3. petals, outside, pollen
4. The top diagram shows fertilisation,
   the bottom diagram shows pollination.
5. tiny, pollen, seeds, sizes, fruit, wide area
6. Clockwise from the bottom left: 4, 3, 2
   fertilisation — 4
7. parent, new, pollination, fertilisation,
   stamen, stigma, pollen, ovary, seed

Page 6 — Asexual Reproduction in Plants

1. pollination, egg, little bit, asexual
2. A, D
3. Growing new plants from cuttings of a parent plant.
   Growing new plants from bulbs.

Pages 7-9 — Taking Cuttings

1. Depends on your experiment.
2. leaf, stem, root
3. Depends on your prediction. There is no right answer.
4. days, dry
5. Each drawing should be neat and fill at least half the box.
6. Depends on your results.
7. Depends on your prediction.
8. Depends on your results.

Section 2 — Life Cycles

Page 10 — Life Cycles of Mammals

1. The monkey, cat, antelope and hamster should be circled.
2. fertilised egg ⟶ kitten ⟶ cat
3. 'The baby hatches from an egg' should be ticked.

Page 11 — Life Cycles of Birds

1. From left to right: 3, 1, 5, 2, 4
2. C, D, A, B
3. E.g. the Dodo didn't have any predators.

Page 12 — Life Cycles of Insects

1. Clockwise from top: caterpillar, chrysalis, butterfly, eggs.
2. These words should be circled: adult, larva, no, adult.

Page 13 — Life Cycles of Amphibians

1. pond, gills, swimming, legs, shrink, froglets, lungs, adult
2. Because the tadpoles are turning into frogs.
   They came from eggs (frogspawn) in the pond.

Pages 14-15 — Life Cycles of Animals

1. The kingfisher, fly, butterfly, frog
   and ostrich should be circled.
2. yes, chick
   fruit bat
   fruit bat
   E.g. it doesn't hatch from an egg or it doesn't lay eggs.
3. Fox — A, Bee — D, Duck — B, Toad — C
4. E.g. a frog's eggs hatch into tadpoles but a chicken's eggs
   hatch into chicks. / The life cycle of a chicken has three
   stages but the life cycle of a frog has four stages.

Pages 16-17 — Life Cycles of Plants

1. Seed dispersal — the seed is moved
   away from the parent plant.
   Pollination — the plant receives pollen from another flower.
   Growth — the seedling grows into an adult plant.
   Fertilisation — the pollen joins with an egg to make a seed.
2. sexual reproduction
3. germination — growth — pollination — fertilisation —
   seed dispersal
   Any flowering plant, e.g. sunflower, apple tree.
4.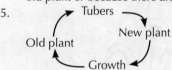
   asexual reproduction
   E.g. because the new plant grows from a little bit of the
   old plant or because there are no seeds in the life cycle.
5. Tubers ⟶ New plant ⟶ Growth ⟶ Old plant

Section 3 — Human Growth

Pages 18-19 — Human Growth

1. A — infancy — 0 - 2
   B — childhood — 3 - 12
   C — adolescence — 13 - 17
   D — adulthood — 18 - 64
   E — old age — 65+

Life Cycles of Animals

3. Here are four **different** animal **life cycles**.

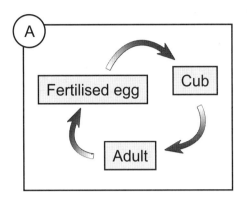

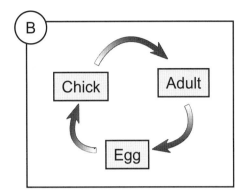

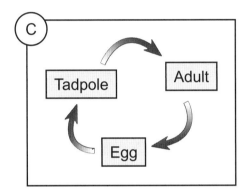

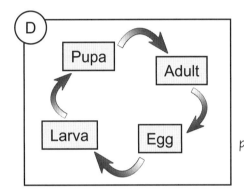

In a butterfly's life cycle a larva is a caterpillar and a pupa is a chrysalis.

Write the correct letter below each animal to match it to its life cycle. Use each letter once.

Fox   Bee   Duck   Toad

....

4. Write down **one difference** between the life cycle of a **frog** and the life cycle of a **chicken**.

If you're struggling with this question, try drawing out the life cycles for each first.

....

....

INVESTIGATE ....

Write down the life cycle of a frog and a butterfly. Make a list of the all the differences in their life cycles. Can you think of any similarities in the way they develop?

Life Cycles of Plants

Plants reproduce <u>sexually</u> or <u>asexually</u>, so they can start life as a <u>seed</u> or as part of an older plant.
When the plant reaches the adult stage, it can <u>reproduce</u> and its life cycle starts again.

1. The pictures below show the different stages in the life cycle of a daisy.
   Draw lines to match each stage to its description. I've done the first one for you.

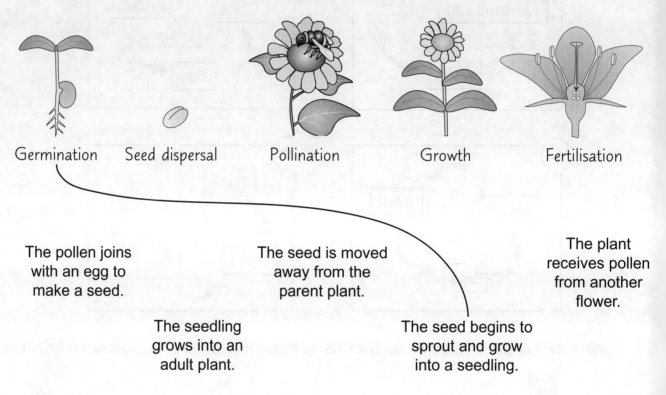

Germination   Seed dispersal   Pollination   Growth   Fertilisation

The pollen joins with an egg to make a seed.

The seed is moved away from the parent plant.

The plant receives pollen from another flower.

The seedling grows into an adult plant.

The seed begins to sprout and grow into a seedling.

2. Are the stages above part of a life cycle using **sexual** or **asexual** reproduction?

   ....

3. What is the correct **order** for life cycle stages of a daisy? Tick (✔) the right box.

   ☐ Growth ⟶ Pollination ⟶ Fertilisation ⟶ Germination ⟶ Seed dispersal

   ☐ Germination ⟶ Growth ⟶ Pollination ⟶ Fertilisation ⟶ Seed dispersal

   ☐ Germination ⟶ Growth ⟶ Seed dispersal ⟶ Pollination ⟶ Fertilisation

   Write down the name of **another** plant that has this life cycle. ....

Life Cycles of Plants

4. Wild strawberries spread overground using **runners**.
    A new plant grows at the end of each runner.
    Complete this **life cycle** for a Wild Strawberry,
    using the words in the box to help you.

Old Plant
New Plant
Runner

....

....

.... old plant ....

....

new plant

runner

growth

Is this sexual or asexual reproduction? ....

Explain your answer.

....

5. Potato plants grow underground **tubers**, which new potato plants can grow from.
    In the box below, draw the **life cycle** of a potato plant.

HINT: use your answer to question 4 to help you.

INVESTIGATE

Make a poster about plant life cycles. Include an example of a plant's life cycle using sexual reproduction and one using asexual reproduction. Draw and label pictures for each stage.

Section 3 — Human Growth

Human Growth

Humans go through different <u>stages of growth</u> in their lives.
When a <u>baby</u> is born, it's helpless, but an <u>adult</u> is able to look after him or herself.

This is Sally in different stages of her life.

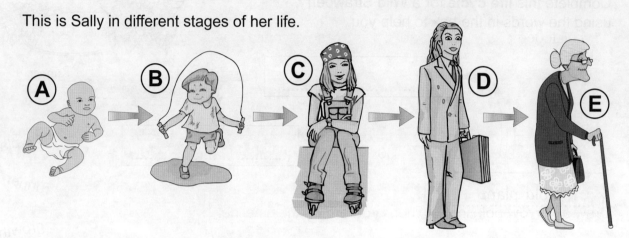

1. Fill in the table about these **stages of growth**.
    The words and ages are in the box below.

    | childhood | 13 - 17 |
    | adulthood | O - 2 | 65+ |
    | 18 - 64 | infancy | 3 - 12 |
    | old age | adolescence |

	Stage of Growth	Age in Years
Ⓐ		
Ⓑ		
Ⓒ		
Ⓓ		
Ⓔ		

2. Write the name of the stage of human growth **you** are at. ....

    Try to think of two people who are at other stages.
    Write down their **names** and the **stage** they are at.

    .... is at the .... stage.

    .... is at the .... stage.

3. Put a letter (**A-E**) next to each of these sentences,
    to show which stage of growth they're talking about.

    goes to primary school ....   doesn't go to work any more ....

    has children that go to school ....   goes through puberty ....

    learns to read and write ....   can't walk yet ....

                    © CGP — not to be photocopied

Human Growth

4. The **timeline** below shows the stages of growth in a **human's life**.
    Draw **lines** to match the name of the stage to its part of the timeline.
    I've done the first one for you.

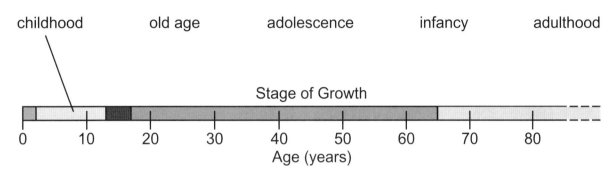

childhood   old age   adolescence   infancy   adulthood

Stage of Growth

0   10   20   30   40   50   60   70   80

Age (years)

Draw an **arrow** pointing to where **you** are on the timeline.

5. Read the information about the people below.

Janet
"I am a great-grandma. I have a grandson called Rob."

Jayden
"I am 8 years old. I have a baby brother called Tommy."

Rob
"I am married and I have two children called Jayden and Tommy.

Tommy

Fill in the table to show what stage of growth you think each person is at.

Name	Stage of Growth
Janet	
Jayden	
Rob	
Tommy	

INVESTIGATE ·

Draw a table with three columns. Ask a friend the names and ages of some people in their family, then fill in the first two columns of your table with that information. For each person, work out what stage of life they are at and write it in the last column.

· ·

Puberty

Puberty is something that happens during <u>adolescence</u>.
It's where children's bodies <u>change</u>, as they develop into adults.

1. Kaye is beginning **puberty**.
    Put a tick (✔) next to the **changes** that will happen to her body.

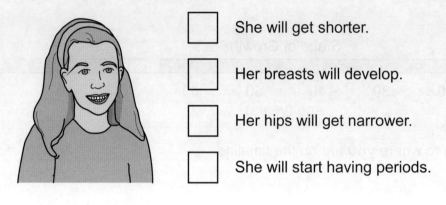

    ☐ She will get shorter.

    ☐ Her breasts will develop.

    ☐ Her hips will get narrower.

    ☐ She will start having periods.

2. Ⓒircle the sentence below which **doesn't** happen during **puberty**.

    The body stops
    growing.

    The body has
    growth spurts.

    The body grows
    more hair.

3. The sentences below are about what happens to **girls** during **puberty**.
    Ⓒircle the right words in **bold** to make the sentences correct.

    During puberty, the **ovaries / breasts** start to release an egg.

    This happens once a **month / year** .

    This is when periods **begin / end** .

4. Mark is beginning **puberty**.
    On this picture, draw what change
    is likely to happen on his face.

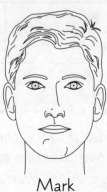

    Mark

   © CGP — not to be photocopied

Puberty

5. At what **stage of growth** does puberty usually happen?

   ....

6. In boys, what do their **testicles** start producing at puberty?

   ....

   Write **two other changes** that will happen to a boy's body during puberty.

   1. ....

   2. ....

7. The sentences below are about what happens during puberty.
   Tick (✔) **true** or **false** for each sentence.

	TRUE	FALSE
Boys develop deeper voices.	☐	☐
Only boys grow body hair.	☐	☐
Only girls start having periods.	☐	☐
Only girls develop bigger muscles.	☐	☐

   Choose one sentence that you've marked as false and write the **correct** version below.

   ....

INVESTIGATE . . . .

Find a picture of a boy, a girl, a man and a woman in a newspaper or magazine.
Write down all the differences that you can spot between the boy and the man, and the
girl and the woman. Circle all of the differences that you think happened during puberty.

Humans and Other Animals

Not all animals take as <u>long</u> as humans to grow up and be able to <u>look after themselves</u>.
In fact, it takes most animals much <u>less time</u> than humans.

This table compares the **development** of some **animals**, including humans.
Look at it carefully and answer the questions below.

Animal	How long the mother carries it before it's born	Time when it can walk	Age when it becomes an adult	How long it might live
Human	9 months	9-16 months	18 years	80-90 years
Sheep	5 months	Within hours	1 year	10-11 years
Elephant	22 months	Within hours	18 years	60-70 years
Horse	11 months	Within hours	5 years	25-30 years
Dog	2 months	3 weeks	1-2 years	11-13 years

1.   Which animal **lives** the **longest**?

....

2.   Which animal is **carried by the mother** for the **longest** time before it is born?

....

3.   Which animals start to **walk** on the same day that they are **born**?

....

4.   Which animal **lives** the **shortest** amount of time?

....

5.   Which animal takes **longest** to **learn to walk**?

....

INVESTIGATE •

- *Copy the table above and add another mammal to it. Use books and the Internet to find out about its development. When you've filled in the table, compare the development of your chosen animal to how humans develop. Which one develops faster?*

Measuring Human Growth

MINI-PROJECT

In this mini-project, you'll look at why the growth of babies is monitored and you'll investigate the difference in height between boys and girls in Year 5.

Read the information in this box, then answer the questions below.

Babies and children go for **regular check-ups** in their first few years of life.
At these check-ups, their **mass** is **measured** and **recorded**.
This is to check that they are **growing** and **developing** at the right **speed**.
If they are **not developing** at the **right speed** it could mean that they have **health problems**.

1. Why do babies and children have their mass **checked regularly**?

   ....

2. Babies should be weighed **without clothes or a nappy**. Circle the reason why.

   Babies don't like   Clothes and nappies   Clothes and nappies
   clothes or nappies.   reduce the baby's mass.   add extra mass.

3. The masses of babies and children are compared to **growth charts**. The growth chart on the right shows the average mass of babies and children up to three years old.

   What is the average mass of a baby at **six months old**?

   ....

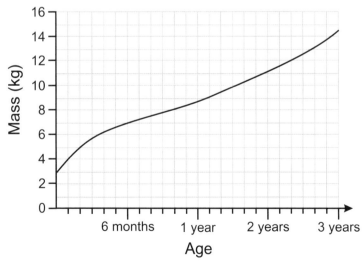

4. Oliver is **six months old**. His mass is **8 kg**.
   Is his mass **higher** or **lower** than the average mass?

   ....

MINI-PROJECT

Measuring Human Growth

In this part of the mini-project you'll **compare** the heights of **boys** and **girls** in **Year 5**. Here's the **method** you should use to get your measurements.

Take your reading to the nearest centimetre.

Measure from the person's heel...

...to the very top of their head.

Use a tape measure.

5. Everyone being measured must **take off their shoes**. Why does this make it a **fair test**?

....

6. You need to measure the heights of **ten girls** and **ten boys** in **Year 5**. Circle the **fairest** way to choose the people to be measured.

Pick all of your friends.

Make everyone stand in height order and pick the tallest people.

Put names in a hat and pick them out at random.

7. Carry out the **measuring** and put your results in these **tables**.

If you can't get these measurements, then use some or all of the spare numbers at the bottom of the page.

	Height (cm)
Girl 1	
Girl 2	
Girl 3	
Girl 4	
Girl 5	
Girl 6	
Girl 7	
Girl 8	
Girl 9	
Girl 10	

	Height (cm)
Boy 1	
Boy 2	
Boy 3	
Boy 4	
Boy 5	
Boy 6	
Boy 7	
Boy 8	
Boy 9	
Boy 10	

Spare Numbers: Girls – 133 cm, 128 cm, 149 cm, 152 cm, 122 cm, 148 cm, 136 cm, 132 cm, 141 cm, 130 cm.
Boys – 134 cm, 119 cm, 126 cm, 151 cm, 119 cm, 132 cm, 128 cm, 134 cm, 140 cm, 129 cm.

© CGP — not to be photocopie

Measuring Human Growth

Now use your results to fill in this table.

Height (cm)	Number of Girls		Number of Boys	
	Tally	Total	Tally	Total
110 - 119				
120 - 129				
130 - 139				
140 - 149				
150 - 159				

Make two **bar chart** of your results.
Plot the girls' scores on the left-hand grid and the boys scores on the right-hand grid.

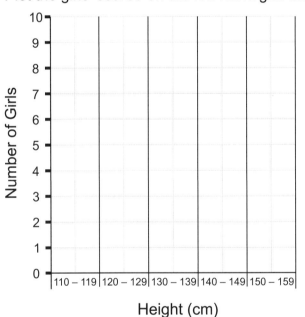

Height (cm)

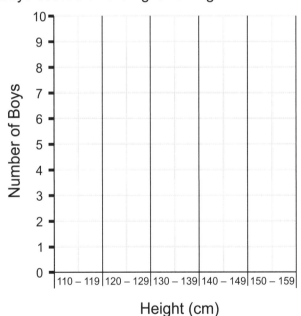

Height (cm)

0. Look carefully at your results. Are the boys or girls taller overall?
    If so, write a **conclusion** for your investigation.

    ....

EXTRA PROJECT

Use your conclusion above to predict who has the higher mass overall in Year 5 — boys or girls? Write a plan of how you would carry out an investigation to compare the mass of boys and girls in Year 5. Say what equipment you would need to use and how you would make sure it was a fair test. Check your plan with a teacher. If you have time, carry out the investigation to see if your prediction is right.

Mixed Questions

*Practice is an important stage in the learning cycle. These pages are squashed
full of questions on stuff you've already done in this book — go get 'em.*

1. (Circle) the mammals below that are in the **baby** stage of their life cycle.

2. Which of these sentences about animal life cycles is **false**? Tick (✔) one box.

    ☐ Eggs are fertilised
    by sperm.

    ☐ All animals are
    born as live babies.

    ☐ Some animals
    hatch from eggs.

3. Complete these sentences about **sexual reproduction**. Use the words in the box to help you

grows	fertilised	seed	female	sperm	ovary	pollen

    Sexual reproduction is when an egg is .... and then

    .... into a new plant or animal. In animals, the egg

    comes from the .... animal and it is fertilised by

    .... from the male animal. In plants, eggs in the

    .... are fertilised by .... from

    another flower. A fertilised plant egg grows into a ....

© CGP — not to be photocopie

Mixed Questions

4.   Look at the fruits and flowers below and write the **name** of the parent plant
     they came from underneath them. Choose plant names from the box.

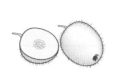

Apple Tree
Dandelion
Gooseberry bush
Sunflower   Tulip

....

5.   Put these stages of **human growth** in the right order.

| adulthood | childhood | old age | adolescence | infancy |

6.   Plants need pollen for sexual reproduction.
     Draw an **arrow** to show where pollen lands on the flower.

     Colour in the part of the flower where **seeds** are made.

     Write down the part of the flower where **pollen** is made.

     ....

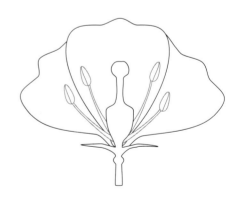

7.   What **stage** of a plant's life cycle is the sentence below describing? ....

          "Pollen travels down into the ovary and joins with an egg to form a seed."

Mixed Questions

8. Fill in the labels for the life cycle of a **frog**.
    I've given the first letter of each word to help you.

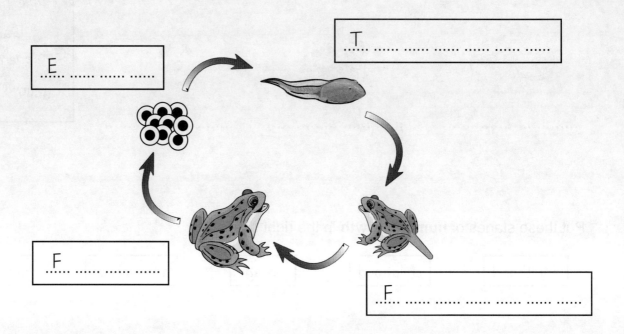

E ....

T ....

F ....

F ....

9. Below are some changes that happen to the body during puberty.
    Complete the table to show which changes only happen to **girls**,
    which changes only happen to **boys** and which changes happen to **both**.

Grow underarm hair.

Breasts develop.

Start making sperm.

Grow facial hair.

Growth spurts.

	Girls	Boys	Both

© CGP — not to be photocopie

Mixed Questions

10. Write **1-4** to put the stages of the **life cycle** of a **flowering** plant in order.
I've done the first one for you.

☐ The seed is moved away from the parent plant.

1 Pollen from another flower joins with an egg to make a seed

☐ The seed grows into a seedling.

☐ The seedling grows into an adult plant.

11. Look at the life cycle diagrams below.

Write down the letter of the diagram that shows
the life cycle of a **butterfly** in the **correct order**. ....

Young dragonflies are called **nymphs**. They hatch from eggs.
Nymphs have legs but no wings, and spend all their time eating.
When a nymph is fully grown, it **sheds its skin** to become an **adult dragonfly**.
How is the life cycle of a dragonfly **different** to the life cycle of a butterfly?

....

....

12. What is **asexual reproduction** in plants?

....

Potatoes can reproduce asexually by growing new plants from tubers.
Write down **another example** of how a plant can reproduce asexually.

....

Glossary

Asexual reproduction	In plants, when part of an **old plant** grows into a **new plant**.
Cutting (plant)	A **piece** cut from a plant.
Fertilisation	When **sperm** (in animals) or **pollen** (in plants) joins with an **egg**.
Germination	When a seed starts to **sprout** and **grow** into a small plant (seedling).
Larva	A **stage** in the life cycle of an **insect**, between egg and pupa. E.g. a caterpillar.
Life cycle	The **stages** that a plant or animal goes through during its **life**.
Pollination	When **pollen** from one plant is carried to the flower of another plant.
Puberty	When the body **changes** and develops during **adolescence**.
Pupa	A **stage** in the life cycle of an **insect**, between larva and adult. E.g. a chrysalis.
Reproduction	Making a **new generation** — animals have babies, plants grow new plants.
Sexual reproduction	When an egg is **fertilised** and then **grows** into a new plant or animal.

© CGP — not to be photocopie